OPEN HIGHWAYS

a diagnostic and developmental reading program

MORE
POWER

Helen M. Robinson
Marion Monroe
A. Sterl Artley
Charlotte S. Huck
William A. Jenkins
Ira E. Aaron
Linguistics Advisor, Andrew Schiller

Scott, Foresman and Company

CONTENTS

4

Pogo Leaves the Circus

Pogo was a clown in a circus.

Every day he rode an elephant.

The elephant's name was Mabel.

Pogo and Mabel were very good friends.

5

At last Pogo got too old to be a clown.
So he had to leave the circus.
He was very sad.
He did not want to leave Mabel.

Pogo thought, "Maybe I can buy Mabel.
Then we'll both be happy.
I'll go ask the man who runs the circus."

"Hello, Mr. James," said Pogo.
"I have to leave the circus.
But I don't want to leave Mabel.
We've been friends for a long time.
Could I buy Mabel and take her with me?"

Mr. James said, "I'm sorry, Pogo.
I can't sell her to you."

Pogo was very, very sad.

7

That night Pogo went to the elephant tent.
He went to say good-by to Mabel.

All at once the lights in the tent came on.
There were all Pogo's circus friends.
  "Surprise! Surprise!" they cried.

And there was Mabel with a big sign
that said TO POGO.

Mr. James said, "This is why
I couldn't sell Mabel to you, Pogo.
Your friends bought her for you.
They bought her as a surprise."

"Oh my!" said Pogo.
"What a fine surprise!"

A clown yelled, "You'd better
save your money, Pogo.
You'll need it to feed Mabel."

Everyone laughed, and Mabel
winked one little eye.

9

Holding Hands

by Lenore M. Link

Elephants walking
Along the trails
Are holding hands
By holding tails.

Trunks and tails
Are handy things
When elephants walk
In circus rings.

10

"Holding Hands" by Lenore M. Link from *St. Nicholas* (June, 1936). Reprinted by permission of Herbert R. Mayes.

Elephants work
And elephants play
And elephants walk
And feel so gay.

And when they walk—
It never fails
They're holding hands
By holding tails.

11

Look! Eddie Can Read

Dad was driving to Grandmother's house.
The car went by a small building.
It had a sign that said RESTAURANT.

"Dad, what's that word?" asked Eddie.
"I can't read it."

"That word is RESTAURANT," said Eddie's dad.
"We'll eat in a restaurant soon."

"Oh!" said Eddie. "I guess I didn't learn that word in school."

"Look! Eddie Can Read" by Ruth C. Kelly (*Highlights*/December, 1961).
Copyright © 1961 *Highlights for Children*, Inc., Columbus, Ohio.

Soon they came to another building.
It had a sign that said MOTEL.

"Mother, what's that word?" asked
Eddie.
"I can't read it."

"It's MOTEL," said Mother.
"We'll sleep in a motel tonight."

"Oh!" said Eddie. "I guess I didn't
learn that word in school."

Soon they came to more buildings. A sign said MIDDLETOWN.

"Mother, what's that word?" asked Eddie. "I can't read it."

"It's MIDDLETOWN," said Mother. "That's the name of this town."

"Oh!" said Eddie. "I guess I didn't learn that word in school."

"Why, Eddie," laughed Dad. "Can't you find any word that you've learned?"

Eddie said, "I'll find one. Just wait!"

There were many streets and many
signs in Middletown.
Dad did not know which way to go.

Eddie said, "There's a word I can
read!"

"Not now, dear," said Mother.
"We're trying to find out which way
to go."

Just then a policeman rode up.
He told Dad to stop.

"Can't you read?" asked the
policeman.
"Didn't you see the sign back there?"

"What sign?" asked Dad.

Eddie said, "That's the one I could
read.   It said STOP!"

"You're right," said the policeman.
"Now, don't let your dad miss
any more stop signs.
Have a good trip!"

Eddie said to Dad, "I knew I would find
a word I could read.
Don't you think I'm a good reader?"

"Yes, you are," said Dad.
"We'll tell Grandmother that you could
read a word better than I could."

Laugh Time

Junk Day on Juniper Street

One morning Davy's father was looking at his newspaper.

"Say!" he said to Davy's mother. "Look at this!"

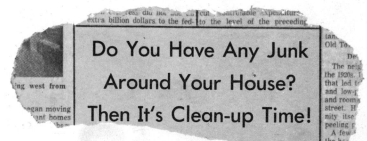

Do You Have Any Junk
Around Your House?
Then It's Clean-up Time!

Davy's mother said, "A clean-up time would be fine."

Adapted from "Junk Day on Juniper Street" by Lilian Moore, from *Humpty Dumpty Magazine* (November, 1964). Reprinted by permission of the author.

Soon Davy's mother went into the yard.
Beth and her mother were going by.

Davy's mother asked, "Did you see
the newspaper this morning?
It said we should have a clean-up time."

"Well, why not?" said Beth's mother.

Some of the mothers came over to see
Davy's mother.
They had seen the newspaper, too.

They said, "We all have junk.
Lots and lots and lots of junk!
Let's clean up!
Let's have a Junk Day on Juniper Street!"

So Juniper Street had a Junk Day.
It was a big clean-up time.

Soon there was junk outside of
every house.
There were old tables, chairs, and toys.
There were all kinds of things.

Davy's father called a junkman.
"Bring a big truck to Juniper Street
tomorrow," he said.
"You'll need it to pick up all the junk."

23

People walked by the piles of junk.

Davy said, "There's a good wheel.

I can fix my wagon with it."

Beth's father saw a toolbox.

He said, "I can fix that toolbox.

It will be as good as new."

Many children found things they liked.
Mothers and fathers found things, too.

Davy's mother found a table.
She said, "That table would look new
with some red paint."

Beth's mother said, "This hatbox
will be fine when I clean it."

The next morning the junkman came.
All the junk on Juniper Street
was gone but one big chair.

"Well, well!" said the junkman.
"This is just what I've been looking for."

He put the chair in the truck.
And off he went with the junk from
Juniper Street.

Ring Toss

Here is a game you can make.
You will need:

an egg carton

3 pencils

a shirt cardboard

tape

scissors

First turn the carton upside down.
Push the point of each pencil into the carton.
Look at the picture to see where to put
the pencils.

Next make three toss rings.
Cut three strips of cardboard 1/2 inch
wide and 13 inches long.

½ inch

13 inches

Bend each strip into a circle.
Tape one end over the other end.

Last, stand back three feet from the
egg carton.
Toss the rings one at a time.
Try to toss the rings over the pencils.
See who can get the most rings over
the pencils.

A Gift You Can Make

You will need:

pencil

spool

a tube of glue

paints

First paint your spool.

Next put some glue on the pencil below the eraser band.

Last, slip the spool over the eraser onto the glue.

The King's Gold

King: Gold!   Gold!
        How I like gold!
        I want more and more!

Queen: You have so much gold now.
        Why do you want more?

King: I just like gold.
        Wise Man, find me a way to
        get more gold.

"The King's Gold" by Sally Jarvis from *Humpty Dumpty Magazine* (September, 1966).
Reprinted by permission of the author.

Wise Man:	Here is a golden pill.
	Eat it!
	Then everything you put
	your hand on will turn to gold.
	(King eats the pill.)
King:	Now let me see what it will do.
	(He puts his hand on the table.)
Queen:	Look! The table turned to gold!
King:	How happy I am!

31

Queen: Oh my! It's time to eat.

King: Yes, I am so hungry!

(He takes an egg.)

Oh! I have turned the egg to gold.

I can't eat it.

Queen: Oh my! Try some hot toast.

(King bites the toast.)

King: Ow! It's hot gold in my mouth!

(Princess comes in. She
runs to her father.)

Princess: Hello, Mother and Father!
I'm ready to eat.

King: No! No! Don't come near me!
(Princess takes her father's
hand and turns to gold.)

Queen: Oh! Our little girl has
turned to gold!

33

King: Help me, Wise Man.

     Give me back my little girl!

     I will give you all my gold.

Wise Man: Are you sure?

     You said that you liked gold

     so much!

King: Not any more!

     I like my little girl more

     than all the gold there is!

Wise Man: Very well.

     (He claps his hands.)

34

(Princess moves.)

King: Thank you, Wise Man.

I have my princess.

Take all my gold.

I never want to see it again.

Hard-Hat Jobs

Some men have dangerous jobs.
Many of them wear hard hats.
The hard hats protect their heads.

These men work in a steel mill.

These men are working on a
tall building.
They are putting a steel beam in place.

This man works in a coal mine.
He wears a mask.
The mask keeps out the dust.
    Can you guess why he has a
light on his hat?

Here are firemen at work.

Can you think of other jobs where men wear hard hats?

Lollipop Surprise

It was Linda's birthday.
She was taking lollipops to school.
She had a bag of lollipops and her books.
They were on the front seat of the car.

Linda's father was a steelworker.
He was on his way to work.
He had a hard hat and his lunch bag.
They were on the front seat of
the car, too.

"Lollipop Surprise" by Marjorie Atkins Elliot (*Highlights*/November, 1966).
Copyright © 1966 *Highlights for Children*, Inc., Columbus, Ohio.

Linda was very happy when she got to school.

She told Mrs. Sims, her teacher, about the lollipops.

Mrs. Sims said, "We will have a lollipop party at milk time."

Linda took out her bag at milk time.
She put her hand in it for a lollipop.
She felt something soft.

Linda looked in the bag.
There was her father's lunch!
There were no lollipops for the children!

"Mrs. Sims!" cried Linda.
"I took my dad's lunch out of the car.
I don't have the lollipops.
Now we can't have a party!
And my dad won't have any lunch."

Mrs. Sims said, "Oh, Linda.
I think the other men will give
your father some lunch.
And we can have your party tomorrow."

Tom said, "Maybe Linda's dad will
give lollipops to the men.
Maybe they will sing HAPPY BIRTHDAY
to Linda."

Mary said, "Let's make pictures!
We can make pictures of the
men eating lollipops."

All the boys and girls made
funny pictures.

The next day Linda gave everyone a
lollipop.
She told what had happened to her dad.

She said, "The other men gave
Dad some lunch.
Dad gave lollipops to the men.
Then they all sang HAPPY BIRTHDAY."

The children thought Linda had
a very fine birthday.

Jimmy's Pocket-Aunt

"Jimmy," said Grandma Jones.
"I'm busy this morning.
You take care of your Aunt Alice."

Aunt Alice was only three years old.
Jimmy was five years older than Aunt Alice.
He did not like to take care of her.
All his friends laughed at him.
They thought it was funny to have
such a little aunt.

Jimmy took Aunt Alice out into the yard.
He began to read, and Aunt Alice played.

Soon Jimmy heard music coming
from the park.
But he did not hear Aunt Alice.
He jumped up and looked around.
No Aunt Alice!

Jimmy ran to the park to look for her.
He could not find her anywhere.

A policeman named Mr. Lee came along.
"What's your name?" asked Mr. Lee.
"And what's the matter?"

Jimmy said, "My name is Jimmy Jones.
My Aunt Alice is lost."

"What does she look like?" said Mr. Lee.
"Is she young or old?"

Jimmy told Mr. Lee what she looked like.
But he did not want the policeman to know
that she was only three.
So Jimmy said, "I guess you could say
that Aunt Alice is young."

The policeman and Jimmy went
into the park building.

"Will Jimmy Jones' Aunt Alice come to
the park building?" called the policeman.

Mr. Lee called four times.
But Jimmy knew Aunt Alice could not
find the park building.

Mr. Lee said, "Just sit there, Jimmy. Lost boys are always found in this park."

"I'm not lost!" Jimmy said. "My Aunt Alice is lost."

Jimmy thought, "Maybe I should tell him Aunt Alice is only three years old."

Just then a policeman walked in. He said, "Here's another lost child."

"That's my Aunt Alice!" said Jimmy.

Mr. Lee said, "What a pretty
little aunt!
I had a little aunt when I was a boy.
I called her my pocket-aunt.
I liked her.
All the other boys wanted
a pocket-aunt like mine."

Jimmy thanked the two men.
Then he started off to his grandmother's house with Aunt Alice.

Jimmy said to himself, "Mr. Lee liked his little aunt.
I like mine, too.
Who said aunts have to be big?
No one!
I'm glad I have a pocket-aunt!"

Candy for Dinner

Tim gave the ball to Mickey.
"I have to go home now," Tim said.
"Dad is bringing Candy for dinner."

Mickey thought, "Candy for dinner!
I wonder what kind it will be."

Tim started to hurry home.

Mickey called to Tim, "May I come for dinner?

I won't eat much!"

"Sure!" Tim said. "Ask your mom!"

So Mickey hurried home, too.

"Mom!" Mickey called from the door.
"May I eat dinner at Tim's house?"

Mother said, "Did Mrs. Blake ask you?"

Ring!   Ring!   Ring!
Mickey answered the telephone.

"Mom!" he said.
"Mrs. Blake said I could come."

"All right," said his mother.

Mickey thought about
big bags of candy
while he dressed.

He thought about
round boxes of candy
when he ran out
of the house.

He thought about deep
dishes of candy on the
way down the street.

He thought about
tall jars of candy
as he knocked
on Tim's door.

55

Tim opened the door.
The two boys went into the dining room.

"Hello, Mickey," said Mr. Blake.
"Candice, I want you to meet Mickey.
Mickey, this is Tim's cousin, Candice."

Candice and Mickey said hello.
Then they all began to eat.
Mickey tried not to eat too fast.
But he kept thinking about the candy.

At last it was time for dessert.
Mrs. Blake came in with a big apple pie.

"How good that looks!" Mickey thought.
"I wonder why they're having apple pie
and candy for dessert.
Well, two desserts are better than one."

Mrs. Blake said, "Mickey, I thought
you and Candy would like this dessert."

Mickey began to laugh.

He said, "The joke's on me!
I thought Mr. Blake was bringing candy
home for dessert.
I didn't know Candy was a girl's name."

Everyone laughed.

Mrs. Blake said, "Come again, Mickey.
Then we'll have both Candy and
candy dessert!"

Peanut Butter Creams

You will need:

a large mixing bowl
a mixing spoon
a measuring cup

a spatula or knife
waxed paper

1/4 cup confectioners' sugar
1 cup chocolate chips

1/2 cup sweetened
    condensed milk
1 cup peanut butter

How to make the creams:

1. First put the confectioners' sugar in the bowl.
2. Add the chocolate chips.

3. Add the milk.
4. Add the peanut butter.
5. Then stir everything together with the spoon.

6. Next drop pieces of candy onto the waxed paper.

7. Chill the candy for a short time.
8. Last, eat your candy.

Sylvester

Sylvester was a little mouse.
He lived in the country because he
loved music.
He loved to hear the songs of the birds.
He loved to hear the wind in the trees.

One day some men came to build
a road.
They dug up Sylvester's home
in the country.
So he went to find a new home in the city.

61

Sylvester looked and looked for a home.
One day he heard music.
The music came from a music store.
Sylvester went in.
The first thing he saw was a guitar.

Sylvester thought, "This will be
a fine house for me.
It has a wire fence in front of the door.
I'll go inside my little house right now!"

Sylvester liked his new house.
He liked going in and out of his door.
He made music when he ran
across the wire fence.
Plink!   Plink!   Plonk!   Plonk!

Every night Sylvester made music
on the wire fence.
People going by the store could hear him.
Plink!   Plink!   Plonk!   Plonk!

People told the storekeeper about the
music they heard at night.
One night the storekeeper stayed
in the store.

Sylvester began to play.   Plunk!   Plunk!
The storekeeper heard the music.
He did not see Sylvester in the dark.

"This is magic!" said the storekeeper.
"A magic guitar that plays by itself!"

Many people heard about
the magic guitar.
A man named Tex heard about it.
He lived way out West.

Tex loved music, and he loved to sing.
But he could not play a guitar.

Tex went to the city.
He found the magic guitar and bought it.
Sylvester was inside sleeping.

Tex started back to the West.
He stopped to rest when it got dark.
All at once Tex heard music.
He sat up and saw Sylvester.

"I don't have a magic guitar!" said Tex.
"I have a magic mouse!"

Tex and Sylvester became good friends.
Sylvester played the guitar, and Tex sang.
They went here.   They went there.
And everywhere they went, they made
music together.

Oh, Susanna!

by Stephen Foster

I come from Alabama with my banjo on my knee, I'm going to Louisiana, my true love for to see.

It rained all night the day I left,

the weather it was dry, the

sun so hot I froze to death,

Susanna, don't you cry.

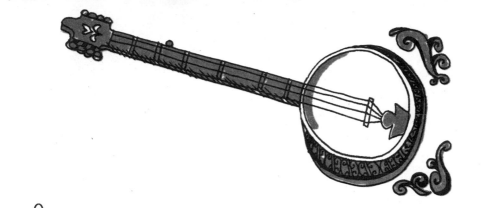

Oh, Susanna! Oh,

don't you cry for me, for I

come from Alabama with my

banjo on my knee.

Pimm
Percy
Patrick
Paul
Pam
Peggy
Patsy
Papa and Mama Pifflesniff

The Seven Little Pifflesniffs

One night the seven little Pifflesniffs were
sniffling and sneezing.

"You children have colds!" said Mama.
"I'll have to take care of you tomorrow.
I won't be able to do my housework."

"Your work is easy, Mama!" said Papa.
"You do my work.
I'll stay home and do yours."

"You'll be sorry," said Mama.

70

The next day the seven little Pifflesniffs
stayed in bed.
Mama went to work in Papa's store.
Papa started breakfast for the children.

"I want scrambled eggs!" said Patsy.
"I want fried eggs!" cried Peggy.
"I want soft eggs!" called Pam.
"I want hard eggs!" shouted Patrick.
"I want boiled eggs!" shouted Percy.
"I want one-minute eggs!" yelled Paul.
"I want two-minute eggs!" yelled Pimm.

"You'll have to wait a while," said Papa.

Soon Papa Pifflesniff brought the eggs.
The children ate them quickly.

"I want milk!" said Patsy.
"I want orange juice!" cried Peggy.
"I want grapefruit juice!" called Pam.
"I want apple juice!" shouted Patrick.
"I want grape juice!" shouted Percy.
"I want hot chocolate!" yelled Paul.
"I want a milk shake!" yelled Pimm.

"You'll have to wait a while," said Papa.

Papa Pifflesniff brought in the drinks.
The children drank them quickly.

"I want my doll!" said Patsy.

"I want my crayons!" cried Peggy.

"I want my book!" called Pam.

"I want my truck!" shouted Patrick.

"I want my marbles!" shouted Percy.

"I want my little cars!" yelled Paul.

"I want water!" yelled Pimm.

"You'll have to wait a while," said Papa.

Papa brought the children's things.
The other children saw Pimm drinking
a glass of water.

"We want some water, too!" they cried.

Papa got the water and began his work.
Just then Mama Pifflesniff came home.

"Oh my," said Papa Pifflesniff.
"It's time for dinner!
The children have just finished breakfast!
And the washing isn't done!"

"Well, Papa," said Mama Pifflesniff.
"I see I'll have to stay home tomorrow
and clean the house!
Now you see it isn't easy for one person
to do all the work."

Papa Pifflesniff gave a big sneeze.
"I think I'm getting a cold," he said.

The next day the children were fine.
But Papa Pifflesniff was still sneezing.

Mama said, "Oh, Papa!
You can't go to work today."

So Papa stayed in bed.

"I want my pillow!" Papa said to Patsy.
"I want my paper!" he cried to Peggy.
"I want my glasses!" he called to Pam.
"I want my pills!" he shouted to Patrick.
"I want water!" he shouted to Percy.
"I want coffee!" he yelled to Paul.
"I want breakfast!" he yelled to Pimm.

The children took care of Papa all day.
Mama did the housework.
And Papa never asked to do
Mama's job again.

Sneezing

by Marie Louise Allen

Air comes in tickly
Through my nose,
Then very quickly—
Out it goes:
Ahhh—CHOO!

With every sneeze
I have to do,
I make a breeze—
Ahh—CHOO!   —Ahh—CHOO!

78

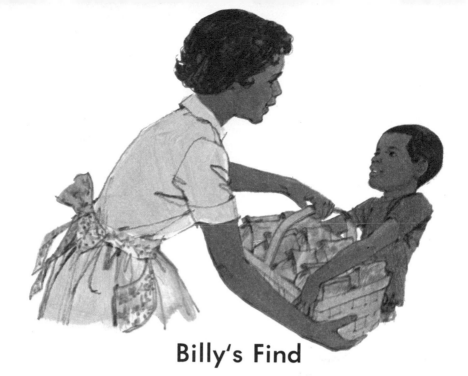

Billy's Find

Mother put ten bags of doughnuts
in Billy's basket.
"There's one bag for every house
in this block," she said.

Billy said, "Mrs. Day won't take one.
She told me not to come by again."

"Then stay away," said Mother.

Billy left with the doughnuts.

79

Billy went along the block selling
his doughnuts.
Soon he came to Mrs. King's house.

Billy thought, "I hope Mrs. King will
buy the last two bags.
I know Mrs. Day won't buy any doughnuts.
And her house is the only one left."

But Mrs. King needed only one bag.
So Billy still had one bag of doughnuts.

Billy started home.
Just then he heard an animal cry.
The cry came from a box outside
Mrs. Day's fence.

Billy saw a puppy in the box.
He picked it up and petted it.
"You look hungry," said Billy.
"Here's a doughnut, puppy.
I'll take you home and give you some milk."

Then Billy saw Mrs. Day looking out of
her window.

He thought, "Mrs. Day might
like this puppy.
She is all alone.
Oh!   She wouldn't want him."

Billy started home again.
Then he walked back and
rang Mrs. Day's bell.

Mrs. Day opened the door.

Billy said, "I'm not selling doughnuts.
I thought you might like this little puppy.
I found him in a box by your fence."

Mrs. Day took the puppy in her arms.
She asked, "Are you sure
you found him?"

"Oh, yes!" answered Billy.

Mrs. Day said, "Well, I'll keep him
if you don't want him."

Mrs. Day looked in Billy's basket.
"I'll buy that bag of doughnuts," she said.

"The bag isn't full," said Billy.
"I gave the puppy one."

"That's all right," said Mrs. Day.
"It's my dog, so I'll pay for a full bag.
And I'll buy a bag every week."

She paid Billy, and he started home.
He thought, "Mrs. Day looks happy now.
And I sold all my doughnuts.
Yippee!"

My Puppy
by Aileen Fisher

It's funny
my puppy
knows just how I feel.

When I'm happy
he's yappy
and squirms like an eel.

When I'm grumpy
he's slumpy
and stays at my heel.

It's funny
my puppy
knows such a great deal.

85

"My Puppy" from *Up the Windy Hill* by Aileen Fisher. Published by Scott, Foresman and Company.

Eating Peanuts with Your Foot

"Can you eat peanuts with your foot?"
Charlie asked.

I said, "I don't know, but I'll try.
Let me take my shoe off."

"No, no," Charlie said.
"You have to do it with your shoes on."

Well, I tried and tried.
But I couldn't do it.

At last I said, "I bet you can't
do it, Charlie."

Charlie just smiled.
He took a board and laid it
over a rock like a teeter-totter.
He put a peanut on one end of the board.
Then he stamped his foot on the other end.
The peanut went right into Charlie's mouth.

That's what I like about Charlie.
Every day I learn something new and
important from him.

Things Not to Do

"I'm making a list of things
not to do," said Charlie.
"It will help me stay out of trouble."

"I'll help you," I said.
"I know lots of things not to do."

Here is the list we made.
You can use this list if you want.
It sure makes life a lot easier for
Charlie and me.
Maybe it will do the same for you.

88

Slightly adapted from *My Friend Charlie*, story and pictures by James Flora, copyright © 1964 by James Flora and reprinted by permission of Harcourt, Brace & World, Inc.

1. Don't tie knots in snakes.

2. Don't step on pigs unless you are barefoot.

3. Don't eat the bottoms of ice cream cones before you eat the tops.

4. Don't put worms in your father's shoes.

5. Don't put peanut butter on horses or turtles.

89

6. Don't dream about monsters.

7. Don't paint your head red.

8. Don't trade your mother
   to gypsies.

9. Don't give bubble gum
   to fish.

10. Don't sit on crocodiles.

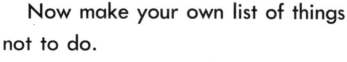

Now make your own list of things
not to do.

Laugh Time Again

Did you know peanuts will make you fat?

How do you know?

Did you ever see a skinny elephant?

Excitement on Appleby Street

Joey walked down Appleby Street.
He thought about his tooth.
It was about to come out.

Joey wanted it to come out so he
could wish on it.
He wanted to wish for some goldfish.

Adapted from *Excitement in Appleby Street* by Eda and Richard Crist. Published by Childrens Press, Inc., Chicago.

Just then Joey saw an open manhole.
There was a fence around the hole.
Red flags and a sign were on the fence.
The sign said MEN WORKING.

Joey looked into the manhole.
Then he sneezed.
His tooth fell out of his mouth.
It fell down into the manhole.

"My tooth!" cried Joey.
"I lost my tooth down there!"

All at once some men inside the manhole started yelling.

"I'll get it," yelled one man.

"Call the police!" cried another man.

Then a man came out of the manhole. He ran down the street.

"It's just a tooth!" called Joey. But no one heard him.

People came running from all over. A big fire truck came around the corner.

Then another truck pulled up.
Men jumped off it with picks and shovels.

Joey did not think about his tooth.
All he thought about was
the excitement on Appleby Street.

A road-breaker came next.
It stopped a few feet from the manhole.
It started to make a hole in the street.

"The water pipe broke!" called a man.
"Turn off the water!"

Some other men climbed down
into the manhole.
And at last the water stopped.

Joey thought, "This excitement was fun.
But I'll go home now.
I guess the men will bring my tooth
to my house later."

Joey went home.
He told his father about his tooth and
about all the men looking for it.

"Oh, Joey!" laughed Father.
"The water pipe broke under
Appleby Street.
The men were running to help fix it.
I don't think they were looking for
your tooth."

"The men won't find it!" cried Joey.
"And I won't get my wish!
I won't get my goldfish."

Father said, "Sometimes a tooth under
the street works fine.
Sometimes it works better than a tooth
under the pillow!"

So that night in bed Joey
went on wishing for
his goldfish.

Morning came.
Joey woke up and looked around
his room.
Yes, the goldfish were there!
Three tiny goldfish in a little bowl!

"Dad was right," thought Joey.
"A tooth under the street works just as
well as a tooth under the pillow.
My goldfish will be as much fun as
all the excitement on Appleby Street."

But Then
by Aileen Fisher

A tooth fell out
and left a space
so big my tongue
can touch my FACE.

And every time
I smile, I show
a space where something
used to grow.

I miss my tooth,
as you may guess,
but then—I have to
brush one less!

"But Then" from *Up the Windy Hill* by Aileen Fisher. Published by Scott, Foresman and Company.

Zoie the Zebra

Zoie the Zebra lived far away
in the jungle.
Other animals lived there, too.
But Zoie was very lonely.
All the animals in the jungle teased Zoie.
They made fun of her stripes.

The monkeys pulled her tail.
They laughed in her ears.

The lion called, "Zoie!   Zoie Zebra!
Why do you wear pajamas with stripes?"

One animal teased Zoie the most.
His name was Henry Hippopotamus.
Henry would laugh at Zoie and
blow water at her.

He would say, "This water will help
you wash off your funny stripes.
Then you will be beautiful like me."

Poor Zoie would wash and wash.
But the stripes would not come off.

One day a man came to the jungle.
He wanted to find an animal for a big zoo.
All the animals came running to see the man.
They wanted to go to the zoo.

But Zoie was shy.
She did not run up to the man.

The man saw Zoie standing alone.
He said, "I like stripes.
That is the animal I like best."

Zoie was very happy.

The other animals were sad.
They wanted to go to the zoo, too.
They wanted stripes like Zoie.

The monkeys painted each other.

Then the monkeys painted the
other animals.

The lion wanted his nose green.
And Henry wanted spots.

The next day the man saw the animals.
He laughed and laughed.
That made the animals very sad.

Zoie didn't want the animals to be sad.
She said, "Please take all of us."

The man said, "OK.
I'll take the other animals, too.
But first they must wash off the paint."

The elephant made a good shower.
He could blow water with his trunk.

It took the lion a long time.
He couldn't get the green paint off his nose!

At last the animals were all clean.
They were ready to go to the zoo.

The other animals said, "Thank you
for your help, Zoie.
We'll never tease you about
your stripes again."

They all started off for the zoo.

Zachary for Z

Zachary was new in the neighborhood.
He was on his way to his new school.
But he did not want to go to school.

"Oh my," thought Zachary.
"I hope no one laughs at my name.
I wish I had a name like Tom, Bill, or Joe!
I'd like any name but Zachary!"

Zachary got to school early.
Many children were playing in the
schoolyard.
But Zachary did not want to play with
them.

Zachary crossed the street and sat
down on a park bench.
He waited for the bell to ring.
He thought, "Will the kids at this school
call me Zachary-Quackery?
The kids at the last school did."

Just then an old man sat down on the
bench beside Zachary.

"Hello, I'm Mr. Sutton," said the man.
"What's your name?
I haven't seen you before."

Zachary looked down at his shoes.
He wanted to say that his name was Tom,
Bill, or Joe.

But he said, "I'm new here.
My name is Zachary Jones."

Mr. Sutton smiled.

"Zachary!" he said.

"What grade are you in?"

"Second," answered Zachary.

Mr. Sutton said, "Well!   Well!
My daughter teaches second grade.
Her class has been waiting for a
Zachary!"

"That's funny!" Zachary said.
"Most kids laugh at my name."

"These children won't!" said Mr. Sutton.
"There's the bell.
Come on!
I'll take you to your room.
I want to see the children's faces when
they hear your name."

Mr. Sutton and Zachary went to the classroom.
The children were in their seats.
Miss Sutton was writing on the board.

Mr. Sutton said, "You have a new pupil this morning, Miss Sutton."

"Hello there," said Miss Sutton. "What's your name?"

"Zachary Jones," answered Zachary.

"Does Zachary begin with a Z?" asked a girl.

"Yes, it does!" answered Miss Sutton.

The children began to clap.
"Zachary for Z!" they said.
"Now we have all of our alphabet!"

Zachary looked surprised.

Miss Sutton said, "We have
twenty-five children in this room.
Each child's name begins with a different
letter of the alphabet.
We were missing one letter.
We were missing the letter Z.
We are lucky you came to our room!"

Zachary was happy.
He thought, "I'm glad my name isn't
Tom, Bill, or Joe.
I'm glad I'm Zachary for Z!"

Pictionary for More Power
Words for People

princess

queen

policeman

king

clown

Words for Animals

crocodile

goldfish

turtle

worm

horse

zebra

hippopotamus

Words for Animals

puppy

mouse

snake

lion

pig

monkey

elephant

Words for Places

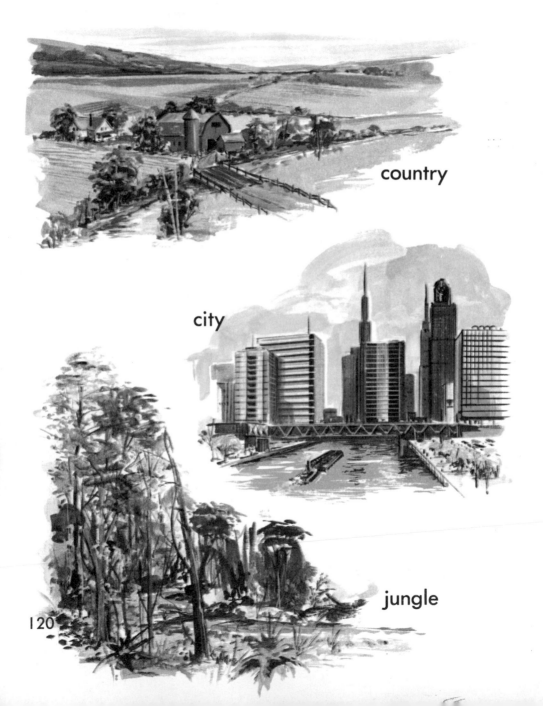

country

city

jungle

120

Words for Things

ice cream

peanut

lollipop

egg

apple

doughnut

bubble gum

grapefruit

pie

grapes

Words for Things

table

pillow

basket

chair

telephone

Words for Things

jar

dishes

glasses

glasses

bowls

Words for Things

teeter-totter

doll

marbles

book

crayons

wagon

124

Words for Things

fire truck

road-breaker

wheel

truck

Words for Things

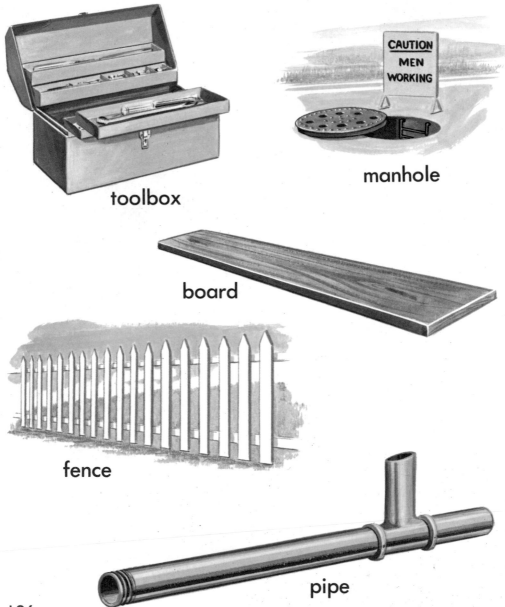

toolbox

manhole

board

fence

pipe

Words for Things

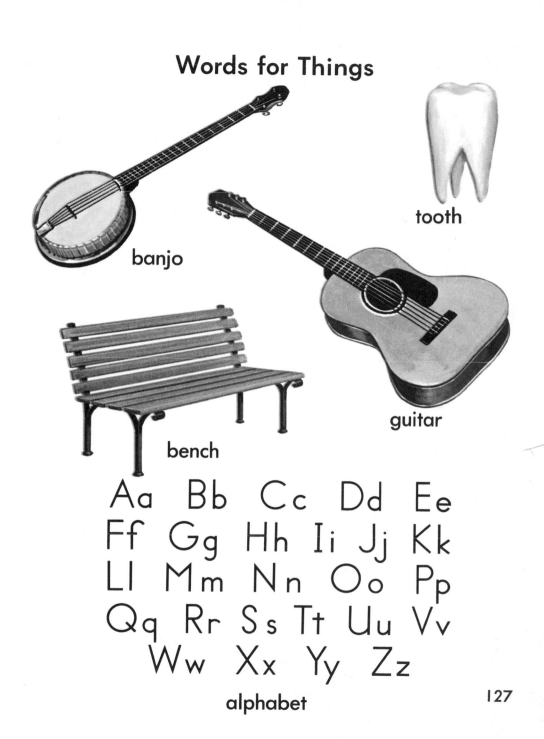

banjo

tooth

bench

guitar

Aa Bb Cc Dd Ee
Ff Gg Hh Ii Jj Kk
Ll Mm Nn Oo Pp
Qq Rr Ss Tt Uu Vv
Ww Xx Yy Zz

alphabet

127

Acknowledgments

Book cover and title page designed by Bradford/Cout Graphic Design.

The illustrations in this book are by:

Justin Wager, pages 5-9
Bob Keys, pages 10-11, 59-60
Jack White, pages 12-17,
    27-29, 110-116
Gene Rosner, pages 18-19
John Solarz, pages 30-35
Lois Axeman, pages 40-44, 85
Tye Gibson, pages 45-51
Joe Rogers, pages 52-58

Rod Ruth, pages 61-66
Bill Peterson, pages 67-69, 91
Dick Scott, pages 70-77
Mary Nolin, page 78
Roy Anderson, pages 79-84
George Suyeoka, pages 92-99
Star Bellei, page 100
Krystyna Stasiak-Orska,
    pages 101-109

The photographs in this book are courtesy of:

Inland Steel Company, page 36
Bethlehem Steel Corporation, page 37
National Coal Association, page 38
New York Fire Department, page 39

6 7 8 9 10 11 12 13 14 15 16 17 18 19 20 21 22 23 24 25   NR   75 74 73 72 71 70 69